Such a Racket!

Written by
Jill Atkins

Illustrated by
Sharon Davey

Ransom

Chung gets on the bus
with his mum.

He rings the bell.

Is Manish at the back?
Is he ringing bells?

Yes, Manish is ringing bells at me.

Is Shep the dog yapping?

Yes, Shep the dog is yapping.

He is yapping at me.

Is that Dan the man?
Is Dan the man banging a can?

Yes, Dan the man is banging a can
at me.

Chung is fed up with the din.
It is such a racket!

Chung yells at Manish
and Shep and Dan.

"Such a racket!
Hush! Shush! Chill!
No din on this bus!"

Manish and Shep and Dan quit
the ringing
and yapping
and banging.

Manish at the back will not be
ringing.

Shep the dog will not be yapping.

Dan the man will not be banging.

9

Chung sits back and gets his hush.

He is not fed up.

Then Chung rings the bell.

He gets off the bus with his mum.